a Night
without armor

a Night without armor

poems

Jewel Kilcher

SCHOLASTIC INC.
New York Toronto London Auckland Sydney
Mexico City New Delhi Hong Kong

ISBN 0-439-10988-4

12 11 10 9 8 7 6 5 4 3 2 1   9/9 0 1 2 3 4/0

Printed in the U.S.A.   40

First Scholastic printing, September 1999

Cover design by Margaret Maclean Mirabile
Interior design by Elina D. Nudelman

THIS BOOK IS DEDICATED TO
  the One in Whom we live and move and have our being
  to my parents, Nedra Carroll and Atz Kilcher
  to my brothers Shane, Atz, and Nikos
  and to the land which inspires my heart to sing, Alaska

Contents

Acknowledgments

The following have my gratitude: My grandmother Ruth Kilcher; my family; Jacqueline Synder; my editor, Mauro DiPreta, and my agent, Sandra Martin; artist Pat Steir; photographer Brigitte Lacombe; Ingrid Sischy; Bridget Hanley; Keith Anderson; BiBi Bielat; Lee Green; and all at HarperCollins and Atlantic Records who have worked to make this book possible.

A Special Note to Young Readers

From an early age, my mother would gather me and my brothers after school for "workshops" in music, visual art, and writing. I grew to love the poems of William Shakespeare, Dylan Thomas, William Butler Yeats, and others that she read to us. She read her own compositions, as well, and taught us to write our own. This led me to understand the strength and soul of poetry: It is something that allows word to be given to things that otherwise have no voice.

Long before I wrote my first song, words formed as poems in my journals, and poetry drives my songwriting today. My songs are strongly influenced by the poems of Pablo Neruda, Octavio Paz, and others. Musically I admire the great poetic lyricists: Bob Dylan, Joni Mitchell, Leonard Cohen, Tom Waits, and many of the writers of Tin Pan Alley, as well as others. Each helped me to connect poetry to music.

To me, poetry is the most honest and immediate art form that I have found. It is a vital, creative expression, and it deserves to be more highly valued, understood, and utilized in our lives.

There is such wonderful poetry in the world that wants to be given voice. In you, there is probably poetry that can be—that should be—given voice.

How do you start to write it? What should you write about? In fact, writing poetry is one of the easiest things in the world to start doing. That's the first thing you need to know. Inspiration can be as simple as a great time you had with your friends or a beautiful day in the park. Inspiration can also come from a really tough time in your life. Sometimes when you're down, putting your thoughts on paper can help you through it.

I take my own inspiration from both the bad times and the good; from lonely times and beautiful times in my childhood—time spent in the inspiring landscape of my homeland, Alaska.

In *A Night Without Armor*, I have collected some of my own writings. It is my hope that as you read through these poems, your own voice will come rushing out and that you will grow to appreciate that voice.

Keep writing always,

Jewel Kilcher

As a Child I Walked

As a child I walked
with noisy fingers
along the hemline
of so many meadows
back home

Green fabric
stretched out
   shy earth
   shock of sky

I'd sit on logs like pulpits
listen to the sermon
of sparrows
and find god in Simplicity,
there amongst the dandelion
and thorn

Paramount, NY, 9:34 A.M.

In the morning tiny bells go off
that light a darkened path
Reluctant as pinpricks
dawn pierces sleep
with nimble fingers
I am unwoven
    the rich yoke of slumber
    unraveled thread by thread
until I am naked and glistening
standing before the newness
of another day
a tiny form birthed of white linen
and restless dreams

Cautious

You don't call

    anymore.
You say
it hurts
    too much
your heart
like one of
those
    fragile cactus flowers
cast amongst
thorny ribs.

So ready
to be
hurt.

Every time her hands began to stutter he became
enraged. She threw these fits sometimes, and he
never took the time to understand what they meant.
Her words were wasted on him. Her hands useless
birds caged by their quietness, and he would
immobilize them, tying her wrists together so they'd
jump like awkward fish, gasping at the shock of air.
Un-heard they'd dance like that for hours, her eyes
full of silent desperation, on the other side of the
closet door. He never even knew what they were
saying.

*I want to fly from here! I want to fly from
here! I want to fly from here! I want to fly
from here! I want to fly from here! I want
to fly from here!*

Dionne & I

We looked in the fridge only to see moldy Kraft singles and some eye cream. That eye cream was our pride and joy, so extravagant and luxurious, it made us feel rich. The cracked walls of the bathroom fading away into the small lights of her tiny vanity mirror.

We may have had no food, but we knew the eye cream was all we needed—we were both young, with pretty faces and a lot of faith in the system.

Some men would take us out.

The Slow Migration of Glaciers

The slow migration of glaciers
unfolding through the centuries
their heavy wing
burdened with all the
weight of the earth
they move and carve and breathe

swollen rivers thick with soot
my pony and I drawing
    deep sharp breaths
as we cross
submerged
in all that is natural and Holy

To run free with you once more
to let my hair tangle itself
in a wind that knows only motion

to lose my heart once again
in the thorns of primrose
on the plains of Fox River Valley
lost in a maze of Timothy and Blue Grass hay.

These are the things which made me
these are the things I call home
these are the things that have filled
my heart with song and I raise them now in homage:

my father and I riding until after dark
chasing cattle or startling eagles into flight
cooking on a coal stove
cutting meat with a dull knife
my hands raw from picking rose hips
on the sea cliffs above Kackamack Bay
staring endlessly at the blue sky . . .

Few would guess now how much I miss
you Alaska

how my heart grows
heavy out here

so far away

So much talk
so much noise
strangling all stillness
so I can no longer
hear the voice of god whisper
to me in the silence

I will return to you, Alaska,
my beloved, but for now
I am youth's soldier
chasing down
an endless dawn

In the South of England Somewhere

In the south of England somewhere
they race lawn mowers
The fastest goes 65 miles an hour
at top speed
with no head wind

I don't know how men run along behind them
Unless it's the kind you sit on—
which seems like cheating

There is a museum there
run by a fanatic
He has memorized and catalogued
the sound each mower makes
noting fondly his favorite three

There are also worm charming contests
Three people to a team
One to charm
one to collect
one to count

Local John McCallister reassures us,
"It's on a strictly catch and release basis, of course."

1966

I turned off the TV.
Looked out of my window
to the streets below.
Dry sidewalks.
A line had straightened up
stiff as uncut ribbon
beneath a sign
that read Army Headquarters.

I stared at the boys' faces.
They looked itchy and awkward
like my brother's. I don't know
what kept them in that line,
the sun was hot and unrelenting.

I wondered if my brother
would stand in line, too.
I wondered if it would take him somewhere.
I wondered if all the brothers
in all the world were leaving,
and if there would only be us sisters left
to occupy the empty rooms
with doll clothing and postcards.

Pretty

There is a pretty girl
on the
Face
of the magazine
And
all I can see
are my dirty
hands
turning the page

Those Certain Girls

I am fascinated by
those certain girls
    you know the ones
the women that are always girls
their tiny bodies like
neglected willow trees
    controlled and contorted
which may blow away with
the slightest disappointment

Sausages

While leaving the airport,
a gypsy woman stole my luggage.
She wore a rice paper mask over her eyes.
A mole showed neatly on her chin,
hairless. She laughed while sausages
fell from her pockets in heavy shivers.
I hope she misses them sorely.

Though I am 8

Though I am 8, my father is 63 years old.
He drinks concoctions of chickweed, garlic, and ordinary grass
pulled out of the front lawn. He blends it with
a machine that wakes me every morning.
It makes a loud growl. He is worried, I think,
he won't make it to my high school graduation.

Outside, winter swallows my footsteps
as quickly as they are laid,
which makes me cry.

We Have Been Called

We have been called
  naive
as if it were
a dirty word
We have been called
  innocent
as though with shame
our cheeks should burn
So
We visited with
the careful idols
of cynicism
to learn to sneer
and pant and walk
  so as not to feel the scales
  of judgment rub wrongly
But we say
  some things must
  remain simple
  some things must remain
  untouched
  and pure
lest we all forget
the legacy which begot us
the health of our origins
the poetry of our fundamental selves

And so
it is to
the longing hearts we sing
rise! spread
your wings!
Let no hand
nor ill will
keep you.

I Say to You Idols

I say to you idols
of carefully studied
disillusionment

And you worshipers
who find beauty
in only fallen things

that the greatest
Grace
we can aspire to
is the strength
to see the wounded
walk with the forgotten
and pull ourselves
from the screaming
blood of our losses
to fight on
undaunted
all the more

You

You with your
    gentle lightning
spinning like Orion,
    full of muscle
and all the patience
    of stars.
Hooked upon the pinnacle
    of a desire
that arrests
    itself,
caught on the crosswires
    of what could be,
my mind turns to you:
    A pin hole of light
    that softly hums
    and murmurs
whose blurry edges
  beg to come into view.

A Slow Disease

My dad went to Vietnam when he was 19 years old.
I think it bruised his soul. There are some things
the human mind should never have to comprehend, some
    things the body never can forget
He doesn't talk about it. Actually, I guess, I've never
    asked,
I hate to imagine his puppy young eyes absorbing all that
    rain and mud and blood.
The jungles must have seemed like a slow disease
that would continue to
arrest his and so many other hearts
the rest of their lives.

I Am Not from Here

I am not from here,
my hair smells of the wind
and is full of constellations
and I move about this world
with a healthy disbelief
and approach my days and my work
with vaporous consequence
  a touch that is translucent
  but can violate stone.

All the Words

All the words I wish your fingers could feel

all the times I've wished
you could know
the silent sorrow
   lying stiff in my throat
like cold
and broken teeth

I wish you could hear
the child that cries
in my flesh and makes
my bones ache

I wish you could speak to my fear

I wish you could hold me
in your arms like oceans
and soothe what my muscles remember
   all the bruises, all the sour hope
   all the screams and scraped knees
the cloudy days so dark
I wondered if my eyes
were even open

The days that I felt
like August, and that I, too
would soon turn
to Fall

You Are Not

you are not
the brave soldier

Neruda's sons
Chaves' brother

you are not
the dark horse
heart filled
with all the weight
and compassion
your hardships
have won you
you are not
driven by the need
to free all people
from meanness and
loveless abuse
        I know you
you are asleep in your church
on Sunday afternoon
looking for god
in answers you seek
through others
instead
of being the answers
you are praying for peace
but unwilling to be it

praying for mercy
but unwilling to give it
praying for Love
but too busy
making sure you got your own:
   a good job
   a good girl
all the trimmings you are
entitled to
all the bells and whistles
that are meaningful
but only to those who possess
a heart most common

The Strip 1

Here I am
on the strip.
The Main attraction.
My name up
in lights.
What's there to do, pussy cat?
   (Nothingnotmuchverylittle.)
My hair is clean
it's the night before
the show.
New Year's Eve.
Downstairs
young people are being young,
gambling, kissing.
I'm in my room eating licorice,
looking at myself
in the mirror,
the flower of youth
sighing and blooming
for hotel art
and stale walls.
What's the news, jack?
   (Nothingnotmuchverylittle.)

The Strip 2

no one slept last night
not hardly
in Las Vegas

what a way to rush in
the new year
Start it off right, right?

I left my hotel
    at 3 A.M.
crossed the street
to buy water
there was a dead body
in the middle of the road
no one had seen it yet
I suppose
but me

The Fall

Labor to open
the large wooden door
wrestle the wind
as it sucks past
and rushes through the house
greedily.

Step into the crisp day
blue sky, dry leaves
   shocked to see
the sun still shining.

It had grown so dark in there

Breathe in deeply,
the thin air
flashing lungs that have been
crying
tied in knots talking to you again again again

We try too hard—
Do you see?

Long Has a Cloak

Long has a cloak of coarse wool
and wet feathers smothered my flight.
Long has doubt and a thorny chain of words
caused my vision to stagger.
Tired of my purple burden,
in search of freedom, I have longed to throw
off the gauze curtains and kisses
which bind me
   my mouth so full of berries
   and other people's tongues
my heart sick with thick hands and spittle.
But there is a secret I do not tell you;
   I have dulled my spark
   and weakened my heart
   so I could continue
   to stay where I knew
   I did not flourish
     (There. It is said.)
To stand new in the naked air
with no crutch, no pretty eye,
I leave not only you
but also the part of me
that fears my own song's truth.

Mercy

I'm leaving

You're done

Cut the cord

I will bare my heart

Make sure it's sharp

Make it quick

Flash your will against me
relieve this red smear
Smother the beating
dull the pulse
Show mercy
Spare it from your side
and I will rip
what was yours, what was living in me,
and return it to you.

Do it while our hearts
are still intact
before they rot in each other's care
before they become riddled with bitterness
choked by the stinking seeds
of resentment.

Freedom

Having mutilated
and freed myself
from the very wings
which for so long
held me aloft
I have cast my heart
like a purpled fruit
toward the violent earth,
far from the Heaven
of your arms

Road Spent

I could stand to be alone
for some time
Lose myself in white noise
slip into the blur
contemplate the color yellow
    Right now
I just don't handle splashes too well
Or too many teeth
around me all at once
armed like guns with something to say
Urgent whispers
hoarse restraint
    Quiet as paper cuts
people steal me away
cart my flesh off in tiny crimson piles
my bones have been sore
Rattling against each other
in their anemic cage
ravens circling
my heart beating
it's-time to-go it's-time to-go
someplace full of surf
full of flat blue sky
full of shuuushhh

Christmas in Hawaii

The sky pierces me
with its turquoise embrace.
The scent of lemons
and suntan oil find
their way to me
by the pool:
No one is here.
I walk the beaches alone
and drink silly concoctions
with little paper umbrellas.
In my room, my guitar
is calling to me.
I will go to it soon
and write songs
for love lost
and for love yet to come.
Merry Christmas, baby,
    goodnight.

Spoiled

I am perhaps
unfaithful
to those who
are outside my
own flesh.

I can not help
it, I am an
opportunist—
each pretty
face should
come with a straw
so that I may
slurp up the
perfect moments
without them getting
stuck between
my teeth.

Saved from Myself

How often I've cried out
in silent tongue
to be saved
from myself

in the middle of the night
too afraid
to move

horrified the answer
may be beyond the
capability of my
own two hands

so small

(no one should feel this alone)

Forgetful

he walks with a skin of stone
in effort to keep his blood
from dirtying the pavement

he closes his eyes
with deliberate determination
trying to remember

the veins behind his eyes
lead like blue road maps
to the ocean of everyone else

Lost

Lost
is a puzzle
of stars
that breathes
like water
and chews
like stone

Alone
is a reminder
of how far
acceptance
is from
understanding

Fear
is a bird
that believes itself
into extinction

Desperation
the honest recognition
of a false truth

Hope
seeing who you really are
at your highest
is who you will become

Grace
the refinement of a
Soul through time

I Don't Suppose Raindrops

I don't suppose raindrops
will ever replace
the sound of small feet

nor sunflowers
their tiny crowns

All the dust has gathered itself
and settled on
   your heart
and there is no correct combination

no key

no question

that will deliver them
once more
to your side

for she has already decided:
   no answers will
   be given

Sometimes

Sometimes
I feel
my heart
fall
to vague depths
between
words there
are such
spaces that
I can't help
but feel
My Heart
fall
between
the pregnant pause
of all you will
not say
and all
I can
not ask

Blanketed by a Citrus Smile

blanketed by a citrus smile
your splash of sincerity evades me
your aim not at fault
I just have no faith left
for it to stick to

it is strange how in just
a few short months
I can look back on myself
like a stranger
        and you
(whom I loved?!)
        are like cumulous clouds
dull day after day
with your threats of thunder
and promises of passion

I await the blue flame!
doused in nutmeg!
wrapped in white linen!

but as you pass over me
there is no torrid sea
no humid embrace

just pools cooling
in the small of my back

I stare at my hands
and wonder
how they got
so far away

The Road

I have just
        caught a glimpse
of what my life
is to become
for a second I could see
        around the curve
and wondered where you were
your bright face
        no longer
beside the road
your hands
        no longer lending
themselves to familiarity

I saw Love
in the rear view mirror
with its red skirt
about its knees
        trying
to catch up
and before the curve
swallowed itself again
I remember
        thinking
There is all this love
but nowhere for it to grow

each second continually
devours the next
and we're moving too fast
for it to fasten
its roots
to the wind

Fragile

Fine. If that's the way you want it.
I will walk away with all the finality
and coldness you accuse me of, but
it won't be what you expect—
a retaliation, a scene, a tangle.
It will be your jaw
flapping like an archaic flag
limp with contemplation.

P.S.

I wrote you those nice
poems only because
the honest ones
would frighten you

Home

Harsh winter falls
away with swollen berries.
My winter-worn tongue gray
with waiting,
dull with no color all
winter long.
Small deep-red watermelon berries
full of blue sky
and all the unfathomable
flavor of spring,
tart green gooseberries and
peach-colored cloud berries
in the fall,
wild blueberries on my chin,
the blush of cranberries high in their bushes.

Stop alongside
the canyon's edge,
lose my fingers in the tangles
of the wild strawberry patch,
my hands deep in
thorny rose hips and raspberries.
Knots of swollen berries
sticking to my stained palms.

August spent
filling empty milk cartons,
canning and preserving
the syrups, jams and jellies
that would sustain us
through another pale December.

After the Divorce

After the divorce
we moved to Homer
to live in a one bedroom apartment
behind Uncle Otto's machine shop.

My brothers slept in the water closet
after my dad painted it any color
they wanted. The pipes looked like
silver trees sprouting up through
the frames of their bunk beds.

For me, we took the door
off the coat closet
and built a narrow bed
four feet off the ground
with a ladder of rough wood
to climb up that hurt my bare feet.
My dad tried hard
to keep us all together
and work at the same time,
but things just weren't the same.
He pulled my hair when he brushed it
and didn't sing to us at night
before we went to sleep.

I was eight and started cooking.
Shane grocery shopped
and Atz, well, he was a kid.
By 7 A.M. every morning
we walked ourselves out to the road
and waited for the school bus
with all the other kids.
Looking for signs
of when life might strike random again
and scatter us like seeds
on the unknowable winds
of chance.

May Brought Longer Days

I

May brought longer days and better chores.
No more throwing hay to the livestock
in sub-zero temperatures, no more waking early
to light a fire, and no more school.

Instead the days were filled with summer work,
good sweaty work: branding cattle, breaking horses,
mending fences that fell in winter.
Long days were spent cutting hay
and raking it into neat rows
to be baled and then hauled into the barn.
Working on my tan, covered in cooking oil,
driving our old tractor, Alice, my eyes would search the
    horizon,
soaking in the ease
of outdoors; of summer and its particular toil.

II

Summer's passing was told in salmon runs,
our subsistence nets on the beach fat with their slippery
    bodies.
Weeks spent bleeding birch trees to make
syrup, canning vegetables
and drying fish in
the smoke house.

Soon the bustle of August rushed us back into our houses where we again became confined to the logs, the coal, and the barrel stove for another long season.

Wolves in the Canyon

During snow storms it is always the most quiet.
Sometimes as a child I would leave my bed
to walk out in the white padded dark
and sit at the canyon's edge, tucked neat
amongst the lacy shelter of tangled willows.

The voice of one wolf can spilt itself so that it sounds like
    the voice of three,
so a small pack of wolves sounds like the most lonesome
    chorus.
Sitting out at the canyon's edge,
looking out upon the still strange landscape of winter,
I knew their song.
I felt it deep in my belly.
Sometimes I was sick with it,
so heavy was it in me that all I could do
was open my mouth and let it call out.
It was instantly my comfort.
My own treasure harbored somewhere
behind my lungs, inside my heart.
It was the song of my soul, I imagined,
and I would lend it to the wolves
and sing with them in the still of midnight,
while my brothers lay sleeping,
beneath thick blankets of dreaming.

Crazy Cow

Shane came back in from evening feed
and said, "Crazy Cow is missing."
Dad finished whatever he was eating
and casually said,
"She is probably calving."

We all knew the odds of
finding the cow in 80 acres
of wooded pasture at night were slim
but still we pulled on our
boots and coats and
headed out with flashlights
into the frozen night.
It was Shane, I think,
who found the calf tangled up in a snow bank,
half alive.
Dad picked it up in one swoop
and looked over his shoulder at the cow.
"Stupid cow," he said.
"Stupid cow," the three of us chimed,
trying not to act amazed.

On the way back to the cabin
the calf quit breathing.
We ran the rest of the way
to the front porch,

the cold air
piercing my lungs and freezing
the little hairs in my nostrils.

Orders were given:
build up the fire,
rub the calve's limbs,
get the blood going.

On the rough wood floor
of that one room cabin
I watched Dad
lean down and wrap his mouth
around the calf's tiny pink nose
fill its lungs,
and then repeat.

His big hands
handled the tiny animal expertly;
the same hands I feared
now seemed more powerful
and merciful than god's.

The Chinese lantern above us
threw a warm glow across the room.
The calf came to, coughing and spitting.
My brothers and I stupid
with giddy emotion.

That night I took a mattress off my bed
and laid it on the floor between Atz Lee and me.

We all watched the calf sleep
and took turns to make sure
it was still breathing.
And all night we dreamt
of all the impossible things
we would do when we grew up.

The Tangled Roots of Willows

I remember as a child
poking at the frozen earth
to expose the roots of willows
encased in glittery sheaths of ice

My father would cut the thin tips
with his pocket knife, wind them
like stiff and knotted rope to carry home

He'd soak them in water for three days
until they were soft
Sometimes using bits of
bone, shell, or feather
as decoration, he taught
us all to weave, many
winter nights spent in
silent concentration

Those were peaceful times,
collecting and unearthing
the tangled roots of willows
in the quiet of night
just my old man and I,
not a thing wrong in the world

Steady Yourself

Steady yourself, love,
steady yourself
for victory is near
Shut out the world
with its tyranny
of noise
     none of this matters now
Draw strength from
the vision the deepest
folds of your soul
so longs for
For it is a song we all sing
Steady yourself, love,
upon my gaze
in this corridor
& waver not in the face
of the battle cry

We will not be beaten!
Lose not your faith now
for I need it to strengthen my own
and should your steps
falter, mine would
grow lonely in this
world of coal and roses

We are the living
and the living
must love the world
It is our duty
to fill our hearts
with all the anguish and joy
of our brothers and sisters
Steady yourself, love,
be strong beside me
and know that our
unrelenting gives them
dis-ease, and that
the clearer your mouth
raises itself in
songs of freedom
the more others will come to
warm themselves around
the flag of your faith
For our numbers grow
and soon will outweigh
their tattered armies
and I want your heart
to rejoice in its
inevitable victory

Sauna

I used to stare up at those cold sharp stars on winter
    nights
stepping naked out onto a cold plank of frozen wood
to escape the heat of the small sauna
which served as our bath every Sunday night.
A turkey thermometer
mounted on one of the four benches
told us how hot it was in there.

We would drink bitter birch sap
mixed with water to cool our insides.
But when the heat became unbearable,
my family and whatever neighbors came
would step outside the door.
Some would roll in snow banks,
some would jump through the thin crust of ice
in the plastic-lined homemade pool that was so cold
it felt like your heart would explode.

Being shy, I'd try and wait to take a sauna until the others
    had finished
and gone inside for thick slices of bread and stew.
Dry heat warming my bones,
mending unknown trespasses.
I would wait until my heart raced with heat and fever
then I would step into the black endless night

letting the cold air rush against my body, steam
rising noiselessly. The mountain ash tree
rustling a few frozen leaves, brittle chimes in the evening
   breeze.

Goodness
(A Poem for Shane)

My older brother Shane
has always been kind
and would shoulder the lion's share
of our many chores.
Come morning
it was his voice
which would rush my consciousness
into the cold reality of the bedroom we shared.
It was his hands
which would numbly feel for coal
in the still black dawn
to start a fire
and his long fingers
which would grasp the warm pink teats
of the milk cow in the freezing cold
so that I could siphon off the cream
to make butter before school.
He broke up fights between Atz Lee and me
absorbing the kicks and screams
and hollers of rebuttal
without anger.
He was our smiling Buddha
a kind constant force in a house
that was otherwise capricious.

I recently went to the hospital
to see his fourth child,
a girl, being born.
I think I am still a child
scattering myself thin.
But as I watched my brother
with his tiny new baby
and his three boys coming up
to take a peek at their new sister
I thought to myself, he must be
a particular kind of being
a breed of person that is made simply
and perfectly to love.

Miracle

Listen!

Do you hear it?
I do.
I can *feel* it.
I expect a miracle is coming.
It has set loose this restlessness
inside of me.

Expect it.
Dream about it.
Give birth to it in your being.
Know! Something good
is coming down the line.
Finding its way to you
like all things find their way
to god's children.

Listen!